THE BABY BOOK

Illustrated by
Jane Winton

TED SMART

This edition produced by Ted Smart
for The Book People Ltd,
Guardian House,
Borough Road,
Godalming,
Surrey GU7 2AE

ISBN 1-85613-080-0

Manufactured in Spain

Producer : Ted Smart
Illustration : Jane Winton
Designer : Sara Cooper
Author : Deborah Gray
Production Assistant : Seni Glaister

**This book is dedicated to
Joseph Robert Cooper**

**The publishers wish to thank
Jane Winton and Bernard Thornton Artists Ltd
whose hard work and co-operation
made this book possible.**

Photograph of your baby

INTRODUCTION

Becoming a parent is a wonderful experience and watching the tiny baby learn to use his own body and relate to the world around him will bring great joy. You will glow with pleasure and pride as he smiles for the first time, when he makes a grab for your finger and later, when he takes his first step. Take the time to record all these milestones in your baby's development as it all passes so quickly. In this record book space has been provided for you to write down your feelings and thoughts along with your own survival tips as you become an expert on babycare. These records and notes may come in handy next time and they will certainly bring back the memories in years to come.

The information contained in this book is not comprehensive, but hopefully will provide a few hints and ideas to help you through the first months – if you are concerned about your baby's health or development, seek professional advice. If you are a first time parent and feeling inadequately prepared – don't fret, you and the baby will learn together over the next few months. Even the most confident parents worry about their babies and if you do have a problem, talk it over with friends and health professionals, they may have some ideas on how to remedy your situation, and in return you may be able to help them with their problems. Remember that this is your baby, and surprising as it may seem, you will be the best judge of what he needs and responds to. Listen to advice, read up on babycare, but most important of all, learn to trust your own instincts.

THE NEW ARRIVAL

Name

Date of birth

Day of birth

Time of birth

Place of birth

Weight

Length

Colour of hair

Colour of eyes

Baby's first photograph

THE NEW ARRIVAL

The last few weeks before the baby is born are full of mixed emotions – excitement and anxiety, happiness and fear. Life will never be the same again, even if this is not the first baby. Use the last weeks to prepare emotionally and practically for the new baby.

Before the birth get to know what baby equipment is now on the market. Ask shop assistants for demonstrations and compare prices. Do ask other mothers for advice – it may well save you making a costly mistake. Also go to an old-fashioned lingerie department and have yourself properly fitted for feeding bras.

When it comes to clothing, remember that babies dislike having their clothes changed and that they are not co-operative. Choose vests with envelope necks that are cosy fitting while easy to pull over the baby's floppy head. Body suits are a good choice as the poppers under the nappy keep the vest in place and the baby snug. Young babies are best in baby grow suits which are warm, soft and simple, those with poppers all the way up the front and down the legs are easiest to change. You will also need little matinee jackets and bootees to go on top of the suits in cooler weather. For taking the baby out you will need a warm snow suit or knitted pram suit and a snuggly fitting woollen hat. Babies lose much of their body heat through their heads so this is essential even when the weather is not really cold.

Any clothes you have in addition to the basic layette are an added bonus and take some of the pressure off the need to wash daily (or even more frequently!). Friends with babies may pass on clothes, even if you do not like the idea of hand-me-downs, accept them as they may be barely worn at all and you will be glad of them when the washing machine breaks down!

Basic Layette

4 vests or body suits
4 babygrows
6 bibs
3 matinee jackets
2 pairs bootees
1 hat
1 pair mittens
1 snow suit or warm jacket and leggings
Shawl or soft blanket to wrap baby

For sleeping the baby will need a moses basket or carrycot which is small and easy to move about the house. You do not need to buy a cot for several months yet. Choose fitted cot sheets and cellular blankets. It is better to use several blankets in preference to a baby duvet as this system enables you to regulate the amount of warmth to the baby's needs. You will want a pram or pushchair, possibly a sling, and maybe a car seat. A bouncing chair is not essential but it is a nice thing to have for the baby who will enjoy watching the world around him.

You may want to prepare a nursery for the baby, but do not feel pressurized into doing so as you will probably have the baby sleeping with you for the first few months. Remember that the nursery or baby's sleeping place should be kept warm day and night 20°C/68°F is perfect. The room used for changing should also be kept warm.

Tips

If you have central heating which you do not want to run continuously, get a portable electric radiator which can be placed in the room where your baby is sleeping.

If you are having a summer baby, buy a large piece of fine muslin and neaten the raw edges. Use in place of a shawl to wrap the baby securely. It doubles as a sheet, is useful to hide under when breastfeeding or it can be draped over the pushchair or carseat as an emergency sunshade.

A packet of 6 muslin squares are handy, use when feeding to catch the dribbles, place in the cot under babies head to cut down on the need to change sheets and place on the changing mat to prevent baby's head being in touch with cold plastic.

If you live in a tall house, have a fully equipped changing station upstairs and down.

Buy unisex clothes that could be used for the next child.

Other Essential Equipment

Changing mat
bath
sponge
soap & shampoo or baby bubble bath
2 soft towels
small bowl for topping and tailing

THE FIRST IMPRESSIONS

Mother

Father

Family and friends

Family resemblances

Name chosen by and reason

First photograph of new family

First photograph of new family

First photograph of new family

First photograph of new family

FIRST IMPRESSIONS

Your first days with your child will probably be spent on the hospital postnatal ward. This is the lull before the storm so do make the most of the time. The staff on the ward will show you how to change nappies, bath and feed the baby. If you are a first time mum, do not hesitate to ask for advise however silly your concerns – the staff are there to help you.

While in hospital ask the staff to help you try to breast feed your child. It is a more discreet, simple and even enjoyable process than you might think. Some babies find the sucking process instinctive while others need help and coaxing, this is true for breast and bottle fed babies. Just be patient, feeding will become easier for both of you with practice.

Many new mums feel frightened at the responsibility of caring for the baby and inadequate due to their lack of experience in handling a newborn. Try not to let these feelings get the better of you as everyone experiences them to a greater or lesser extent. Do not be surprised if you do not feel the intensity of love for the baby that you were expecting, sometimes this takes time to develop and in no way means that you are unnatural. Remember that you have experienced a great many physical and emotional changes over the past months and you should not be surprised if you feel exhausted and depressed. It is quite natural to want time to recover, instead you are deprived of a good night's sleep and have a new baby to cope with. Talk to someone about how you feel – it is very common especially about three days after the birth.

If you have older children then it is important to plan how to introduce them to the baby. If they come to visit at the hospital, try to have the baby in the cot so that you can devote all your attention to them for a few minutes before showing them their new brother or sister. It is a good ploy to have a present from the new baby to the older child, a baby doll is a good gift as the child can be encouraged to mimic you with your baby.

When you go home it is also important to give the older child your full attention for a while, he has probably missed you terribly while you were at the hospital. Sibling rivalry is inevitable, be patient, be fair and try to see the situation from the point of view of the older child. You will have limited time for the bigger child, but try to talk to him while you are caring for the baby, give him as much positive feedback as you can so that he still feels like an important person in your life.

BEAUTIFUL BABY

Your first photographs of the baby are likely to be snap shots taken soon after the baby is born. As such they are wonderful keepsakes but it is unlikely that they are worthy of framing.

Good baby photographs do depend to some extent on luck, but they can be planned. Natural light is preferable to flash light which produces a hard feel to the photographs unsuitable for baby photographs. Choose a bright day and select the brightest area of your house taking care to avoid harsh sunlight. Make a set for the baby to lie on. Spread blankets on the floor and place the baby in the centre, have a look through your camera and make sure that there are no bits of carpet or edges of chair legs showing. Create a soft feel by gently arranging creases in the blankets around the baby. If the light reading on your camera is still just below 1/60th second, then make a reflector by hanging a white sheet or baby blanket on a chair back near to the baby and get down low to take the picture, this should reflect some of the light back onto the baby. Proceed to take your photographs. If you have a camera with adjustable exposures, take a few photographs at stops either side of the recommended exposure.

If you are in a situation where you have to use a flash, try to get someone to attract the baby's attention so that she is not looking at the camera. This reduces the risk of 'red eye'. If you are taking photographs of mother and baby, have the mother looking at the baby rather than at the camera, it creates a nice feel as well as avoiding red eyes.

When photographing outside it may be beneficial to use the flash even on a bright day if there are a lot of strong shadows. Use a flash too if taking a picture into the pram where it is darker than the surrounding area, alternatively use a slightly longer exposure, although this will blank out the background.

Tips

All baby photographs are hit and miss, they suddenly move or screw up their faces so take plenty of shots.

Once the baby is old enough to sit up and respond, visit a professional photographer for a set of really good baby pictures – a framed picture makes a great Christmas present for doting family.

A set of photographs of a wakeful young baby in the bouncing chair are good as they show the baby taking notice of the world around her.

Look through your baby books and parenting magazines as they are full of lovely baby pictures. These will give you ideas for your own poses.

If you have only got a simple camera, ask a friend who knows about photography to come and shoot off a reel of your baby.

BABY'S BIRTHDAY

ASTROLOGICAL GUIDE

Astrological sign	Date
Aquarius	January 21 - February 19
Pisces	February 20 - March 20
Aries	March 21 - April 20
Taurus	April 21 - May 21
Gemini	May 22 - June 21
Cancer	June 22 - July 23
Leo	July 24 - August 23
Virgo	August 24 - September 23
Libra	September 24 - October 23
Scorpio	October 24 - November 22
Sagittarius	November 23 - December 22
Capricorn	December 23 - January 20

BIRTHSTONES AND FLOWERS

Month	Birthstone	Birth flower
January	Garnet	Snowdrop or Carnation
February	Amethyst	Violet or Primrose
March	Aquamarine	Jonquil
April	Diamond	Sweet Pea or Daisy
May	Emerald	Lily of the Valley
June	Pearl	Rose or Honeysuckle
July	Ruby	Larkspur or Water Lily
August	Peridot or Sardonyx	Poppy or Gladiolus
September	Sapphire	Morning Glory or Aster
October	Opal or Tourmaline	Calendula or Cosmos
November	Topaz	Chrysanthemum
December	Turquoise	Holly or Narcissus

OUR BEAUTIFUL BABY

Astrological sign

Birthstone

Birth flower

At birth   *At three months*

Colour of hair

Colour of eyes

Colour of eyelashes

Colour of eyebrows

Complexion

Distinguishing marks

FAMILY ALBUM

Mother

Father

Grand-parents

Grand-parents

Great Grand-pa

Great Grand-ma

Great Grand-pa

Great Grand-ma

Grand-pa

Father

Sisters

Great Grand-pa

Great Grand-ma

Great Grand-pa

Great Grand-ma

Grand-pa

Grand-ma

Mother

Brothers

Baby

BABY'S FIRST DAYS

Visitors

Gifts

Flowers

KEEPSAKES

Hospital bracelet

Lock of hair

Birth announcement

FEEDING BABY

Breast feeding is undoubtedly best for baby, so do give it a try. As soon as possible after the baby is born he should be put to the breast to encourage his rooting and sucking reflexes. He does not receive milk at first but colostrum, which is a combination of water, vitamins, minerals, protein and antibodies which prepares his digestive system for the milk which comes in about three days after birth. There is no artificial substitute for colostrum.

When the milk first comes in the breasts often become painfully hard and swollen. This is due to the increased activity in the breasts as you begin to produce milk and will subside within a few days when the supply and demand system becomes established (you will have to go through this period of engorgement even if you decide to bottle feed). The more your baby sucks, the more milk you will produce for his next feed and once the feeding routine is established you should not suffer discomfort although you will feel full as the next feed approaches. As the baby grows and needs more milk, your body automatically produces sufficient, and until the baby is about 12-14 weeks or has doubled his birthweight, breast milk should provide all the nutrients your baby requires.

If you run into problems with sore nipples or the development of tender patches on the breast, speak to your midwife or doctor as soon as possible, they should be able to help.

Advantages of breast feeding

Breast milk is what nature intended for the newborn baby. It contains the correct balance of nutrients and is easy to digest. At the beginning of each feed the baby receives fore-milk which is thirst quenching followed by hind-milk which is higher in calories and satisfies the baby's hunger.

The milk contains the mother's antibodies which protect the baby from many infections. There is also evidence to suggest that breast fed babies are less likely to grow up suffering from various conditions such as allergies, asthma and eczema.

Breast milk is always available.

Breast milk is very inexpensive. You just have to make sure that you eat well and drink regularly. You may also need a mid-afternoon rest to keep up energy levels and milk supplies for the evening.

Advantages of bottle feeding

The baby's father, friends and relations can feed the baby for you giving you time to rest or go out for a few hours.

You can tell exactly how much milk the baby is drinking.

It is more socially acceptable than breast feeding.

Tips

To prevent soreness in the first weeks, allow your nipples to dry in the air, then apply little camomile ointment.

If you intend to return to work or plan on leaving the baby in the first months, encourage the baby to take a bottle containing boiled water or expressed milk in the first few weeks, otherwise she may reject the teat altogether.

When making up formula milk, prepare enough bottles to last for the next 12 hours.

Avoid warming baby's bottles in the microwave as the heat is not evenly distributed and may burn the baby's mouth.

There are a number of support groups and telephone help lines for the breast feeding mother. Speak to someone who understands the problems before giving up breast feeding the baby.

A large shawl-type scarf is great to drape over your shoulder and cover the baby to provide a private tent under which to feed the baby. Using this method you can do it literally anywhere!

It is easier and more discreet to breast feed in loose baggy clothes rather than front opening blouses.

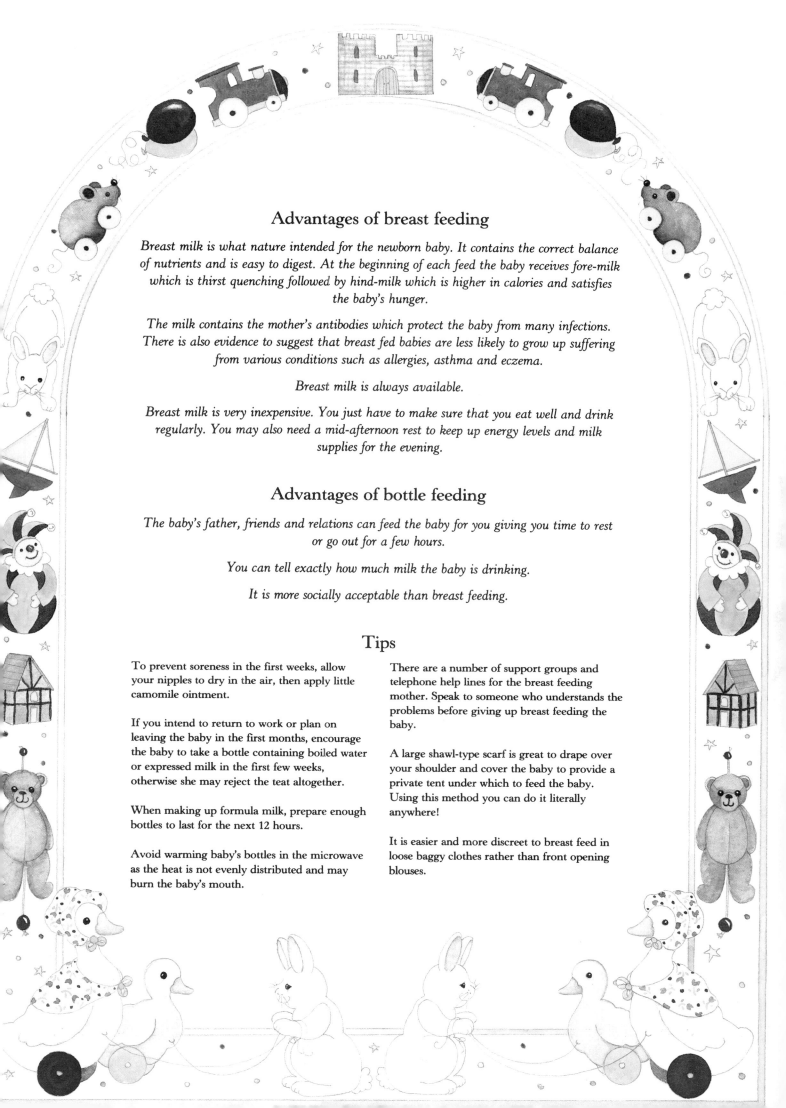

THE BOTTOM LINE

The prospect of spending the next two years nappy changing does not fill any parent with joy. For this reason the majority of people choose to use disposable nappies. They are now very efficient, simple to change, require no washing but are expensive.

Traditional terry squares are still popular. You will need at least two dozen, preferably three, as well as plastic pants and pins. It is sensible to use disposable one-way nappy liners to make cleaning easier. A more recent invention is the shaped terry nappy which is easier to put onto a wriggling baby, there is no need for pins as the nappies are secured with a velcro strap. There are also flannelette versions of this on sale. It is worth buying good quality plastic pants as they tend to last longer than the cheaper ones. You will also need a bucket with a lid and sanitizing powder.

Then there is the green debate. Disposable nappies use vast quantities of wood pulp and plastic and they are difficult to dispose of. Manufacturers stress that the wood pulp used in nappies comes from managed, renewable forest, that non-chlorine bleach is now used to whiten the pulp and that the use of absorbent crystals has reduced the amount of wood pulp used. However energy is still required to produce the nappies and to transport them to your home. Maybe of greater concern is that research suggests that as much as one-third of solid waste on community disposal sites consist of disposable nappies. These contain untreated human waste which in time may seep into the soil and contaminate ground water supplies.

On the other hand, terry nappies are not environmentally friendly either. After they are rinsed off they sit in chemical sterilising solution until they are washed in a detergent – usually on a hot or boil programme and then they have to be dried. In summer and if you have a garden then this is a simple process, but if you have to use a dryer then you are using still more energy.

When it comes to changing time, it is best to have a changing station where all your lotions and potions are on hand. This is best done in a bathroom or toilet where you have access to water. First of all clean off the baby's bottom using either moist cotton wool or a baby wipe taking care to check all the creases. Remember to wipe girls' bottoms front to back to prevent vaginal and bladder infections. Pat the area dry, including the creases. Next apply a barrier cream to prevent the bottom from becoming sore from prolonged exposure to moisture, apply in a thin layer all over the bottom, using too much cream is wasteful. A good regime is to use simple petroleum jelly most of the time – this is an excellent barrier, it is inexpensive, and makes cleaning dirty bottoms easier. Then, if the bottom looks a little red use an antiseptic cream and on very sore bottoms use a camomile-based ointment. If the nappy rash persists, speak to the doctor as it may be a fungal infection which needs treating with special creams. Finally, package your baby's bottom up in the nappy of your choice, wash your hands and relax until next time.

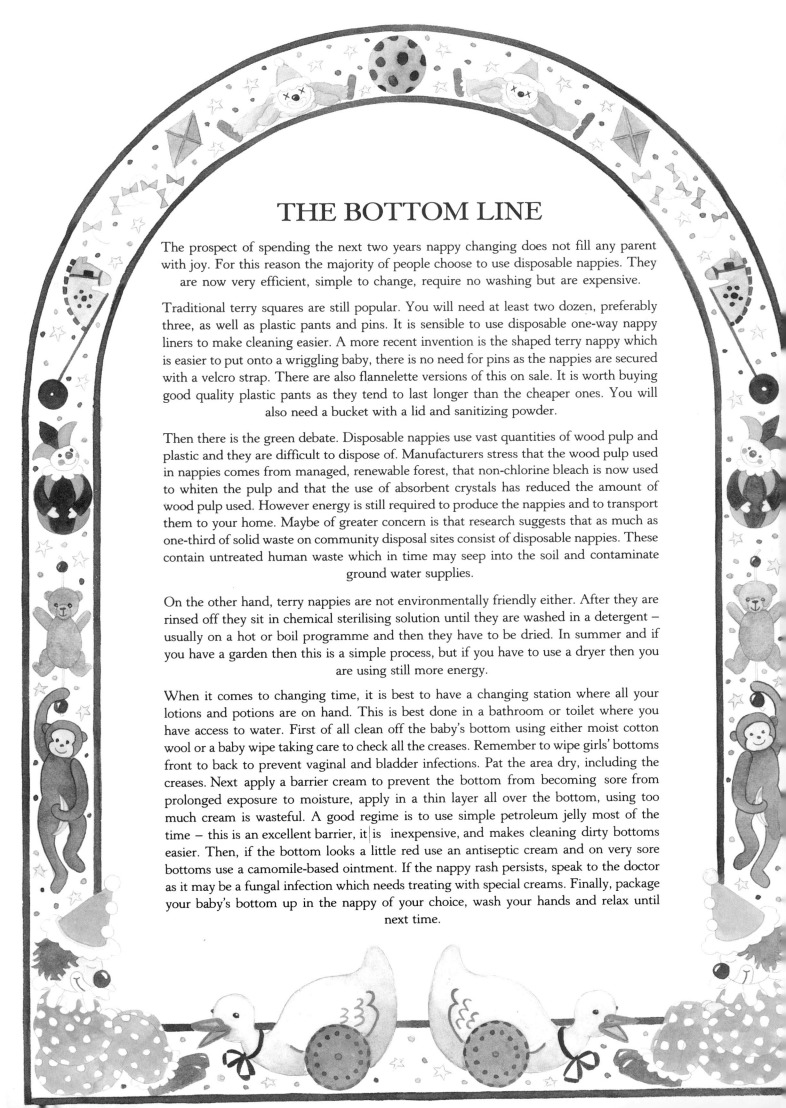

KEEPING CLEAN

Until you are confident in handling your baby, bathtime might fill you with apprehension. You may be advised to avoid emersion bathing until the cord drops off, towel bathe and top and tail your baby instead.

Whatever variety of cleansing you have in mind you should always prepare yourself in advance. Increase the heat in the room to about 21°C/70°F. Place a towel on the changing mat to take off the chill and have a chair ready for your own use. Collect together all the items that you will need:

Baby soap or baby bath liquid   *Soft sponge or flannel*   *cotton wool*
2 towels (one for use and one in reserve)   *Nappy changing gear*   *Full set of clothes*

Topping and Tailing

In addition to the above you should also have two bowls of clean water. Undress your baby down to his vest then take a clean piece of cotton wool, moisten in the water then carefully wipe one eye. Repeat for the second eye using fresh cotton wool and clean water. Next wipe the mouth, nose and ears, avoid cotton buds as these may cause damage to tiny babies. Finish wiping the baby's face and neck with water only and pat dry. Wash and dry the baby's hands.

Remove the baby's nappy and wash the entire bottom thoroughly with soap or baby bath liquid. Rinse well with clean water and pat dry. Change the baby's vest if necessary and dress the baby.

Towel Bath

Have to hand the items listed above plus two bowls of clean, warm water. Lay a towel over your changing mat and remove all the babies clothes except the nappy. Wash the face, neck and hands as for topping and tailing. Remove the nappy, then clean the nappy area with water from one bowl only and set that bowl aside. Then wash the baby's body all over with soap paying particular attention to the creases under the arms and in the thighs. Rinse the soap off very thoroughly. Pat the baby's body dry as you go along.

Baby's Bath

Wrap the baby's body in a towel with him still on your lap, wash his face as for topping and tailing. Now hold his head over the water supporting his neck with your hand and holding his body firmly in position under your arm. Using your free hand, wet his hair and wash with shampoo or baby bath. Wash off the soap.

Now support his neck in the crook of your arm and place him in the water, Wash with a soapy sponge making sure that all the creases are well washed and rinsed. Return the baby to your knee and wrap in a towel and dry very thoroughly especially in those creases. Use this opportunity to be close to your sweet-smelling baby.

BABY'S
NEW WORLD

News headlines

_____

_____

_____

Prime Minister

Opposition leaders

World leaders

Actors

Actresses

Top films

TV programmes

Pop stars

No. 1 record

Sports stars

Standard prices

milk   bread   nappies   jeans

Place newspaper headline from day of birth here

Place weather report from day of birth here

BABY'S FIRST HOME

Date   Time

Weather

Baby's outfit

Who took Baby home

How

Baby's first address

Baby's first home visitors

Nursery decorations

Photograph of Baby's first home

Pat-a-cake, pat-a-cake, baker's man,
Bake me a cake as fast as you can;
Pat it and prick it and mark it with T,
Put it in the oven for teddy and me.

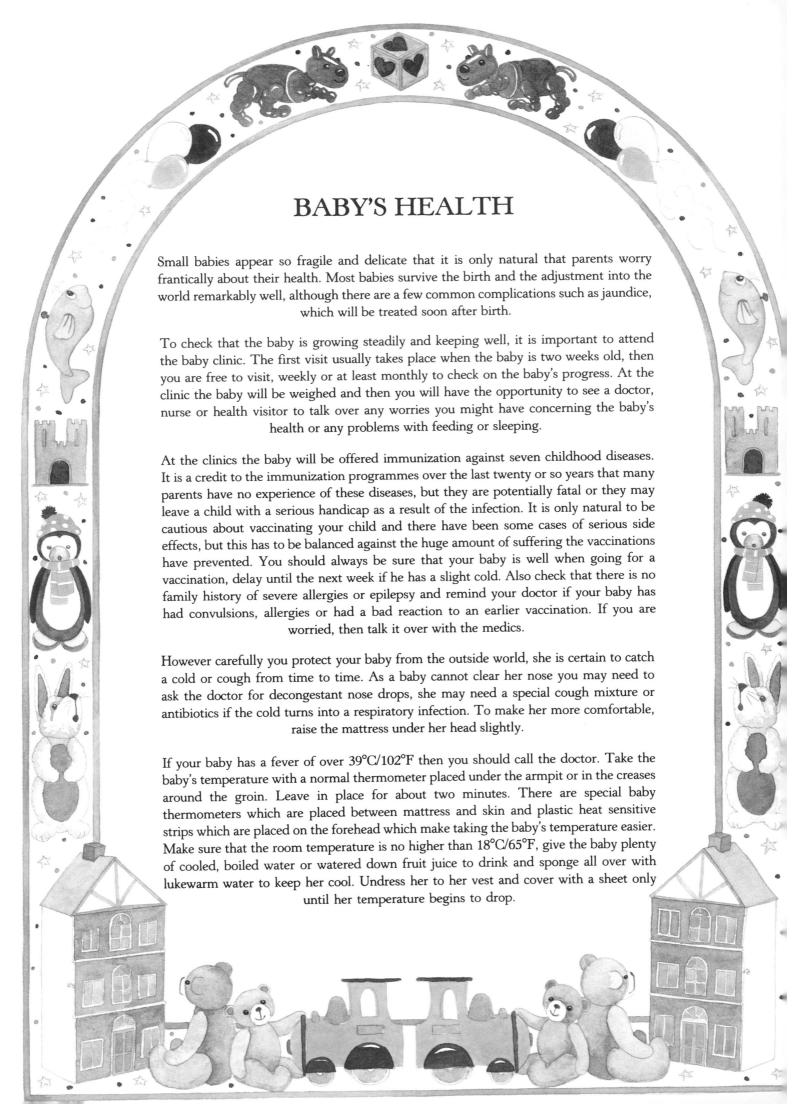

BABY'S HEALTH

Small babies appear so fragile and delicate that it is only natural that parents worry frantically about their health. Most babies survive the birth and the adjustment into the world remarkably well, although there are a few common complications such as jaundice, which will be treated soon after birth.

To check that the baby is growing steadily and keeping well, it is important to attend the baby clinic. The first visit usually takes place when the baby is two weeks old, then you are free to visit, weekly or at least monthly to check on the baby's progress. At the clinic the baby will be weighed and then you will have the opportunity to see a doctor, nurse or health visitor to talk over any worries you might have concerning the baby's health or any problems with feeding or sleeping.

At the clinics the baby will be offered immunization against seven childhood diseases. It is a credit to the immunization programmes over the last twenty or so years that many parents have no experience of these diseases, but they are potentially fatal or they may leave a child with a serious handicap as a result of the infection. It is only natural to be cautious about vaccinating your child and there have been some cases of serious side effects, but this has to be balanced against the huge amount of suffering the vaccinations have prevented. You should always be sure that your baby is well when going for a vaccination, delay until the next week if he has a slight cold. Also check that there is no family history of severe allergies or epilepsy and remind your doctor if your baby has had convulsions, allergies or had a bad reaction to an earlier vaccination. If you are worried, then talk it over with the medics.

However carefully you protect your baby from the outside world, she is certain to catch a cold or cough from time to time. As a baby cannot clear her nose you may need to ask the doctor for decongestant nose drops, she may need a special cough mixture or antibiotics if the cold turns into a respiratory infection. To make her more comfortable, raise the mattress under her head slightly.

If your baby has a fever of over 39°C/102°F then you should call the doctor. Take the baby's temperature with a normal thermometer placed under the armpit or in the creases around the groin. Leave in place for about two minutes. There are special baby thermometers which are placed between mattress and skin and plastic heat sensitive strips which are placed on the forehead which make taking the baby's temperature easier. Make sure that the room temperature is no higher than 18°C/65°F, give the baby plenty of cooled, boiled water or watered down fruit juice to drink and sponge all over with lukewarm water to keep her cool. Undress her to her vest and cover with a sheet only until her temperature begins to drop.

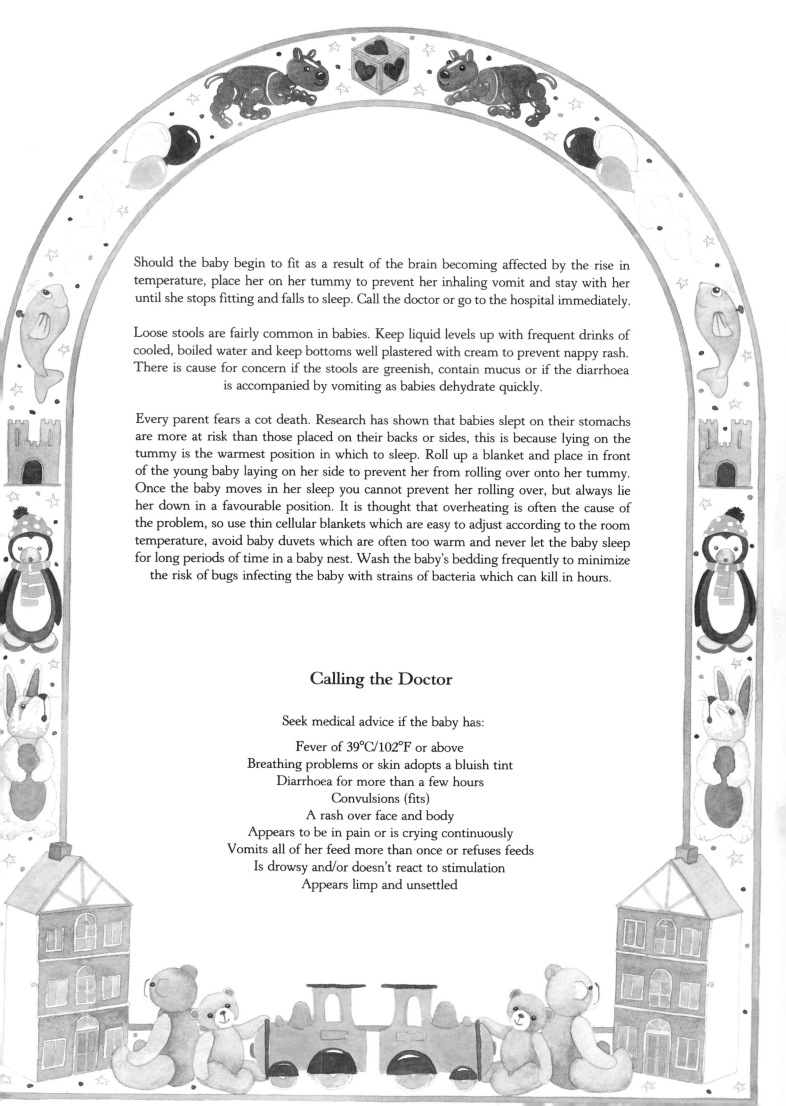

Should the baby begin to fit as a result of the brain becoming affected by the rise in temperature, place her on her tummy to prevent her inhaling vomit and stay with her until she stops fitting and falls to sleep. Call the doctor or go to the hospital immediately.

Loose stools are fairly common in babies. Keep liquid levels up with frequent drinks of cooled, boiled water and keep bottoms well plastered with cream to prevent nappy rash. There is cause for concern if the stools are greenish, contain mucus or if the diarrhoea is accompanied by vomiting as babies dehydrate quickly.

Every parent fears a cot death. Research has shown that babies slept on their stomachs are more at risk than those placed on their backs or sides, this is because lying on the tummy is the warmest position in which to sleep. Roll up a blanket and place in front of the young baby laying on her side to prevent her from rolling over onto her tummy. Once the baby moves in her sleep you cannot prevent her rolling over, but always lie her down in a favourable position. It is thought that overheating is often the cause of the problem, so use thin cellular blankets which are easy to adjust according to the room temperature, avoid baby duvets which are often too warm and never let the baby sleep for long periods of time in a baby nest. Wash the baby's bedding frequently to minimize the risk of bugs infecting the baby with strains of bacteria which can kill in hours.

Calling the Doctor

Seek medical advice if the baby has:

Fever of 39°C/102°F or above
Breathing problems or skin adopts a bluish tint
Diarrhoea for more than a few hours
Convulsions (fits)
A rash over face and body
Appears to be in pain or is crying continuously
Vomits all of her feed more than once or refuses feeds
Is drowsy and/or doesn't react to stimulation
Appears limp and unsettled

TEETHING

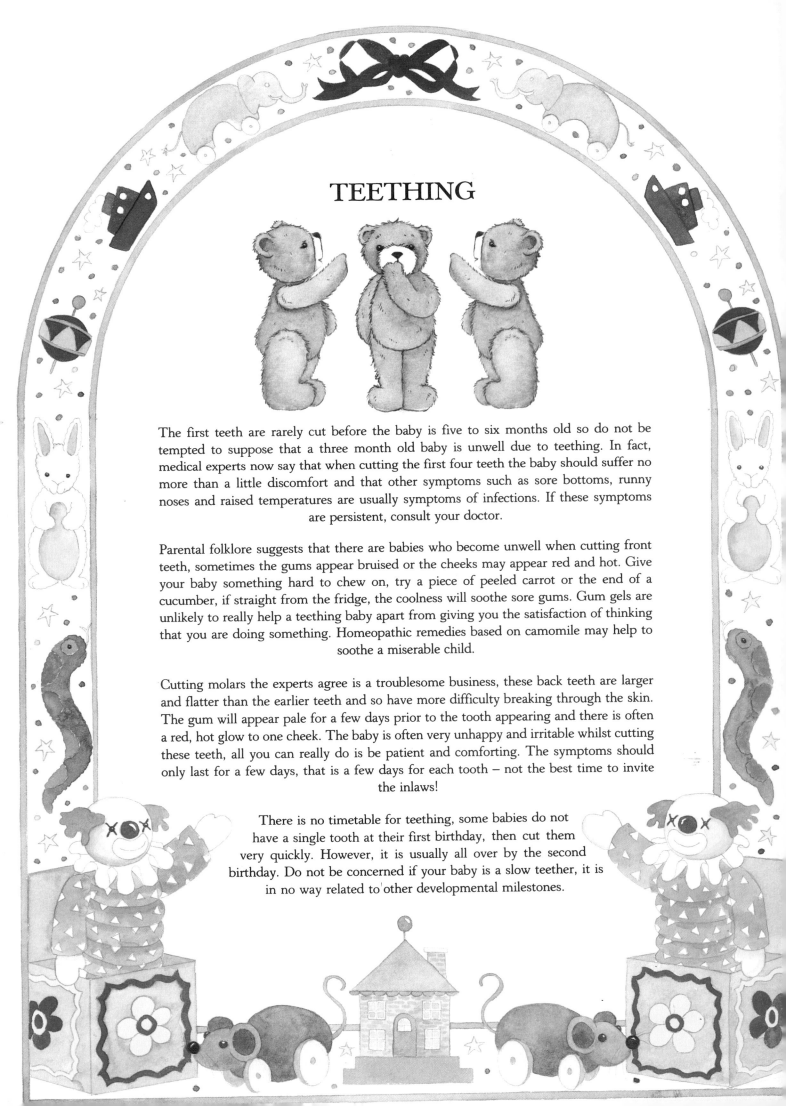

The first teeth are rarely cut before the baby is five to six months old so do not be tempted to suppose that a three month old baby is unwell due to teething. In fact, medical experts now say that when cutting the first four teeth the baby should suffer no more than a little discomfort and that other symptoms such as sore bottoms, runny noses and raised temperatures are usually symptoms of infections. If these symptoms are persistent, consult your doctor.

Parental folklore suggests that there are babies who become unwell when cutting front teeth, sometimes the gums appear bruised or the cheeks may appear red and hot. Give your baby something hard to chew on, try a piece of peeled carrot or the end of a cucumber, if straight from the fridge, the coolness will soothe sore gums. Gum gels are unlikely to really help a teething baby apart from giving you the satisfaction of thinking that you are doing something. Homeopathic remedies based on camomile may help to soothe a miserable child.

Cutting molars the experts agree is a troublesome business, these back teeth are larger and flatter than the earlier teeth and so have more difficulty breaking through the skin. The gum will appear pale for a few days prior to the tooth appearing and there is often a red, hot glow to one cheek. The baby is often very unhappy and irritable whilst cutting these teeth, all you can really do is be patient and comforting. The symptoms should only last for a few days, that is a few days for each tooth – not the best time to invite the inlaws!

There is no timetable for teething, some babies do not have a single tooth at their first birthday, then cut them very quickly. However, it is usually all over by the second birthday. Do not be concerned if your baby is a slow teether, it is in no way related to other developmental milestones.

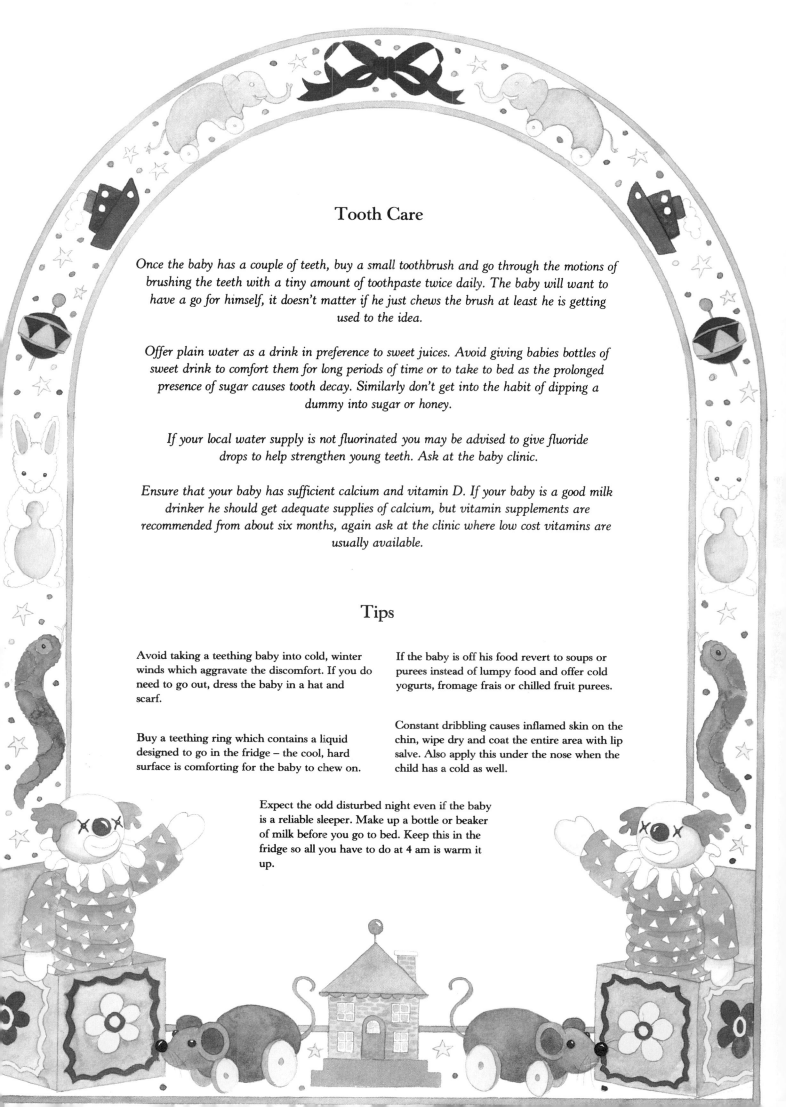

Tooth Care

Once the baby has a couple of teeth, buy a small toothbrush and go through the motions of brushing the teeth with a tiny amount of toothpaste twice daily. The baby will want to have a go for himself, it doesn't matter if he just chews the brush at least he is getting used to the idea.

Offer plain water as a drink in preference to sweet juices. Avoid giving babies bottles of sweet drink to comfort them for long periods of time or to take to bed as the prolonged presence of sugar causes tooth decay. Similarly don't get into the habit of dipping a dummy into sugar or honey.

If your local water supply is not fluorinated you may be advised to give fluoride drops to help strengthen young teeth. Ask at the baby clinic.

Ensure that your baby has sufficient calcium and vitamin D. If your baby is a good milk drinker he should get adequate supplies of calcium, but vitamin supplements are recommended from about six months, again ask at the clinic where low cost vitamins are usually available.

Tips

Avoid taking a teething baby into cold, winter winds which aggravate the discomfort. If you do need to go out, dress the baby in a hat and scarf.

Buy a teething ring which contains a liquid designed to go in the fridge – the cool, hard surface is comforting for the baby to chew on.

If the baby is off his food revert to soups or purees instead of lumpy food and offer cold yogurts, fromage frais or chilled fruit purees.

Constant dribbling causes inflamed skin on the chin, wipe dry and coat the entire area with lip salve. Also apply this under the nose when the child has a cold as well.

Expect the odd disturbed night even if the baby is a reliable sleeper. Make up a bottle or beaker of milk before you go to bed. Keep this in the fridge so all you have to do at 4 am is warm it up.

BABY'S
VITAL STATISTICS

Weight   Height

_____
at birth

_____
one month

_____
three months

_____
six months

_____
nine months

_____
twelve months

_____
fifteen months

_____
eighteen months

_____
two years

BABY'S FIRST TEETH

first tooth	second tooth	third tooth
fourth tooth	fifth tooth	sixth tooth
seventh tooth	eighth tooth	ninth tooth
tenth tooth	eleventh tooth	twelfth tooth

BABY'S HEALTH

Visits to the doctor

Date	Doctor's name	Reason

Immunizations

Date	Date	Date
	Diptheria	
	Tetanus	
	Whooping cough	
	Polio	
	Measles, mumps and rubella	

BABY'S DAY

Every baby is different and develops different feeding and sleeping patterns around which you have to continue to run your home and maybe look after others as well. The first few months are never easy and it is a matter of muddling through as best you can. There are times when everyone feels that they cannot cope, that the house is dirty, the ironing isn't done, you haven't washed your hair for days and there is nothing prepared for dinner. Take pride in what you have achieved, namely that you have nurtured a little dependent person through another day, he's fed, warm, clean and loved.

You will have to be adaptable for the first few months, prepare the evening meal in the morning if this is when the baby has his sleep. Don't worry about the dust, just tidy up a bit and keep the kitchen and bathroom clean. Have a few ready made meals in the freezer even if this is not your style, the chaos does not last for ever.

If you are lucky your baby will sleep for a good deal of the time, but some babies never sleep for more than ten to twelve hours a day. If you have a wakeful baby you will find that he will be entertained by watching you and listening to your voice, so take him into the kitchen in a bouncing chair and talk to him while you cook. He will probably be contented if you take him for walks to the shop or happy to watch the leaves on the trees for a time.

It takes time for a routine to be established, but it is a good idea to get the baby to learn the difference between day and night and to recognize sequences of events. A small baby will sleep anywhere at first, let him sleep in a different place during the day from his night-time sleeping place. If you have a pram and a garden, let him sleep outside, providing he is well wrapped up in cooler weather and protected from direct sunlight in summer, he will be fine. Do not leave the baby outside if the weather is damp. Leave a margin of flexibility in the routine you establish otherwise you may find that the baby becomes too dependent upon it, not sleeping in any cot but his own for instance which becomes difficult when you want to go away.

You may have a baby who is fairly contented in the day but needs what seems like constant night feeds. When dealing with the baby at night, keep the lighting as minimal as possible and do not talk or play with the baby so that he begins to learn that this is not the time when he gets much fun out of you. You may find yourself falling to sleep whilst breast feeding the baby, do not worry as providing that you are not drunk or on sedatives you won't roll over and crush the baby. Bottle fed babies too may sleep more readily with you. Some women send their partners to another room for a while so that both of you are not wrecked or if you are bottle feeding you might devise a rota to ensure that you both get some sleep. Just play it by ear and do whatever seems necessary to survive, as the baby begins to sleep for longer spells you will find it easier to get him back into his cot and normal marital relations will ultimately return.

Tips

Mothers should accept all offers of help, let others take the baby for a walk while you take a long bath or catch up on some sleep.

Wrap a young baby securely in a shawl when putting him down to sleep, this makes him feel secure and may encourage him to stop crying and to sleep.

Rhythmical movements such as slow, gentle rocking, walking, patting the back often soothe a tired, crying baby.

Tapes of a mothers heartbeat can be obtained which combined with wrapping may remind the young baby of the security of the womb.

The sucking reflex may soothe the baby, try encouraging him to suck his fingers or you could use a dummy.

Failing all else, take a crying, tired baby for a drive in the car, the motion will send him to sleep.

BABY'S EARLY DAYS

At one week

Sleeping times

Feeding times

Playtimes

Memories

At one month

Sleeping times

Feeding times

Playtimes

Memories

At three months

Sleeping times

Feeding times

Playtimes

Memories

At six months

Sleeping times

Feeding times

Playtimes

Memories

OUT AND ABOUT

It is quite likely that your first journey with your baby will be the journey from the hospital to home and the chances are that this will be by car. For the first nine months the baby's car seat must be facing backwards to put less stress on the baby's back so you have the option of using a baby nest car seat which is designed just for the first months, or a fixed seat which can be turned around when the baby is bigger. The advantage of the nest is that the sleeping baby can be lifted out of the car and carried into the house without waking her up and there are pushchair frames that are adapted to take the nest – if you are very dependent on your car, this is an invaluable option.

Your next need is for a pram or carrycot. Again the main consideration is your lifestyle, if you have a winter baby, you do a lot of walking and envisage sleeping the baby in the garden, then invest in a new or secondhand carriage pram. If you depend on your car, then maybe a carrycot on a frame that will later take a pushchair seat is a better option for you. A carrycot can be fitted to a double buggy so that an older child can ride too, it can be secured in a car and can double as a bed for a young baby. However, if your baby is large at birth, it may last only three months.

If you choose to have a pram, then you will also need a pushchair. You could opt for a very simple umbrella action chair, some of which do have an adjustable back for a comfortable sleep. These are extremely handy, but they are not suitable for babies under about nine months and they have no shopping trolley. A buggy type pushchair with a movable bucket seat is probably the best bet – the simpler the better. You could get away with buying only a reclining pushchair if you are having a summer baby, but they offer too little protection from the elements for an autumn or winter baby.

You may be attracted to the idea of a sling which is excellent for carrying the young baby around as she is comforted by your warmth and your presence. Take time to choose a sling that is easy to slip the baby into and easy for you to wear – Houdini would have problems with some on the market. Some fabric slings can be turned into backpacks for the larger baby suitable from about nine months or you may opt for a framed backpack which is more comfortable to wear and will last until the baby is over two years old – providing you have the strength!

Tips

Take time when choosing a pushchair. Make sure that it is simple to collapse with one hand, that it fits comfortably into your car and that it is easy to keep clean.

Check that the waterproofs for wet weather are durable and easy to use, ask for a demonstration and take care to fit as directed as they are easily torn.

Choose a lightweight pushchair if you rely on public transport.

Make sure that the straps and buckle on the car seat are easy to fasten and unfasten.

In cold weather use a warm sack fitted onto the pushchair in preference to blankets which get thrown off.

A very young baby will look directly at the sun and could damage her eyes so take care not to leave her in direct sunlight without a sunshade.

BABY'S FIRST OUTING

(record the date, reason for outing and Baby's reactions)

First visit to mother's parents

First visit to father's parents

First ride in a pram

First outing in a car

First train ride

First aeroplane ride

Photograph of Baby's first outing

THE DEVELOPING BABY

The newborn baby will lie curled up much as she did in the womb, her hands will be closed, her movements jerky and uncontrolled and her muscles unable to support her head. Over the next few months she will gradually unfold, at about six weeks she will be able to hold her head up for a short time, at around 12-16 weeks she will be able to push herself up on her forearms and by about six months will be sitting supported by cushions. Soon she will lean forward and find herself on her hands and knees and after that will learn to crawl about. By then she will be exploring the world around her and will pull herself into a standing position in order to see more of what is going on. It may still be a few months before this standing progresses into unsupported walking which requires a tremendous amount of muscle coordination and balance. You will suddenly realize that you no longer have a baby, but a toddler.

At about six weeks the baby will open up her fingers, grasping toys and pulling off spectacles. At first she will try to pick up objects with her fist, but gradually she will learn that small objects can be picked up more efficiently using the forefinger and thumb, at this stage she is keen to feed herself with a spoon – you will have entered upon the messy phase.

Even a small baby tries to communicate. She cries when she is hungry, cold or frightened and stops when you pick her up and nestles into the security of your body. You will soon recognize the difference between her hungry cry and her tired cry and will be able to react to her demands. The sound of the human voice, particularly mother's, is fascinating to the baby who stares intently at first then, at about 6 weeks, her face will light up into a definite smile when she is spoken to and she will let out a delighted cooing sound. This is the beginning of language and if you are quiet when the baby 'speaks' then answer her back you will discover that you can converse with your baby long before she learns words.

The first few sounds are soon extended as the baby plays with her vocal skills repeating the sounds then combining them. By ten months or so the baby is constructing sentences of sounds, she is anxious to communicate and will be delighted if you respond by repeating her noises. She will understand a great deal by now, she will respond to her own name as well as recognizing those of other children in the family, she will clap her hands when she hears the command and will open and close her hands in a baby wave when she hears 'bye bye'.

As the baby grows so she spends more time awake taking in the world around her and gradually learning about it through sight, sound, touch and taste. It is important to stimulate all these senses with mobiles, pictures, board books and toys, but the most vital aid to progress is the time that you spend playing with the baby. You will be thrilled with her giggles as you play 'peep boo' from behind a book, and she will learn from you that the duck is pulled by the string and that a tower of bricks can be knocked down and built up again. While you are playing games with her you are talking to her, reinforcing the sounds that she makes and so teaching her the rudiments of language.

Tips

Babies love music and seem to love children's music best of all. Have a tape of nursery songs in the car for long journeys, she'll love them especially if you sing along.

Play physical games with your baby, 'This little piggy went to market' with the toes or 'Row row the boat' with the baby on your knee. This helps them develop and gives them pleasure too.

Once the baby is mobile and pulling himself up you will have to be very careful not to leave small objects within his reach.

A baby will learn daily sequences so it is a good idea to prelude going to bed with a fixed set of events, for instance, a wash or bath, change of clothes, drink of milk in a quiet, darkened room, then lay her down and finish with the familiar sound of a musical toy.

Avoid giving the baby coloured brochures and leaflets as the printing ink may contain lead.

Fill a low drawer with objects that the baby will enjoy playing with, old boxes, spoons, squeeky toys, empty tubes etc.

BABY'S FIRSTS
(record Baby's age)

Recognises mother	Recognises father
Lifts head	Lifts head and shoulders
Notices toys and pictures	Follows moving objects with eyes
Turns head on hearing a noise	First smile
First laugh	First gurgling noise

Memories

Plays with hands

Plays with feet

Eats solid food

Rolls from front to back

Holds a toy

Moves toy between hands

Reaches for toy

Points at objects

Memories

BABY'S FIRSTS

(record Baby's age)

Puts everything in mouth

Holds spoon to eat

Smiles at own reflection

Looks at books

Enjoys splashing in bath

Sleeps through the night

Smiles at strangers

Sits in a high chair

Sits unsupported

Crawls

Memories

Photograph of Baby's firsts

Photograph of Baby's firsts

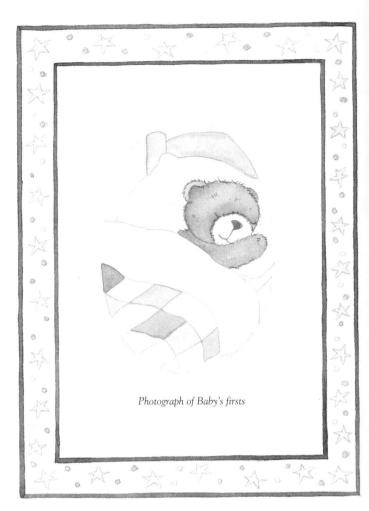

Photograph of Baby's firsts

Photograph of Baby's firsts

Photograph of Baby's firsts

Photograph of Baby's firsts

BABY'S FIRST CHRISTMAS

Where Christmas was spent

Who Christmas was spent with

How Christmas was celebrated

Baby's presents

Baby's reactions

Baby's age

Photograph of Baby's first Christmas

Round and round the garden,
Like a teddy bear,
One step, two step,
Tickle you under there.

BRINGING UP BABY

No one wants a spoilt child, but the small baby is too young to understand cause and effect and so too young to try to discipline. When a baby cries it is because he is hungry, frightened, uncomfortable or simply wants your company. If you think that it is not time for him to wake up and demand your attention he will not understand why, his cries will become more desperate and when you do go to him he will be terribly upset and unable to stop whimpering. Research has shown that babies whose cries are fairly readily met, settle quicker and become confident children, confident because they are secure in the knowledge of your love. It is hard to apply this philosophy at 4am two hours after the last interruption to your sleep, but leaving him is unlikely to reduce his demands for night feeds.

You cannot spoil a baby by loving him too much. Some babies go through a phase at eight to ten months when they want constant cuddles and cry if you leave the room. You will need patience to get through this phase, but the baby will settle down and learn to play by himself more quickly if you give attention when he feels he needs it. Place him in the highchair at your side while you are preparing meals and keep him entertained with a piece of carrot, a spatula or a few teaspoons – talk to him or sing nursery songs, ultimately it is easier than having him clasping your knees in floods of tears.

You may worry that devoted grandparents buy too many toys, while he is a baby he will not understand, he will just enjoy the selection of shapes to hand, if he is dressed like a prince, you can be certain that he will not appreciate it. Similarly, if his toy box consists of rattles made from washing-up liquid bottles and beans, he will be enthralled and will be totally oblivious of his hand-me-downs – all the baby needs are objects to satisfy his curiosity and your attention.

As the baby grows into a toddler then you do have to begin to lay down guidelines. Tell grandma that coming laden with gifts on every visit is unhelpful, you want the child to enjoy her company not anticipate what she has in her bag. Do not be tempted to keep the baby quiet by constantly feeding biscuits, or buying him a treat every time you go to the shops. These soon become habits and very hard to break once the baby is a demanding, vocal toddler.

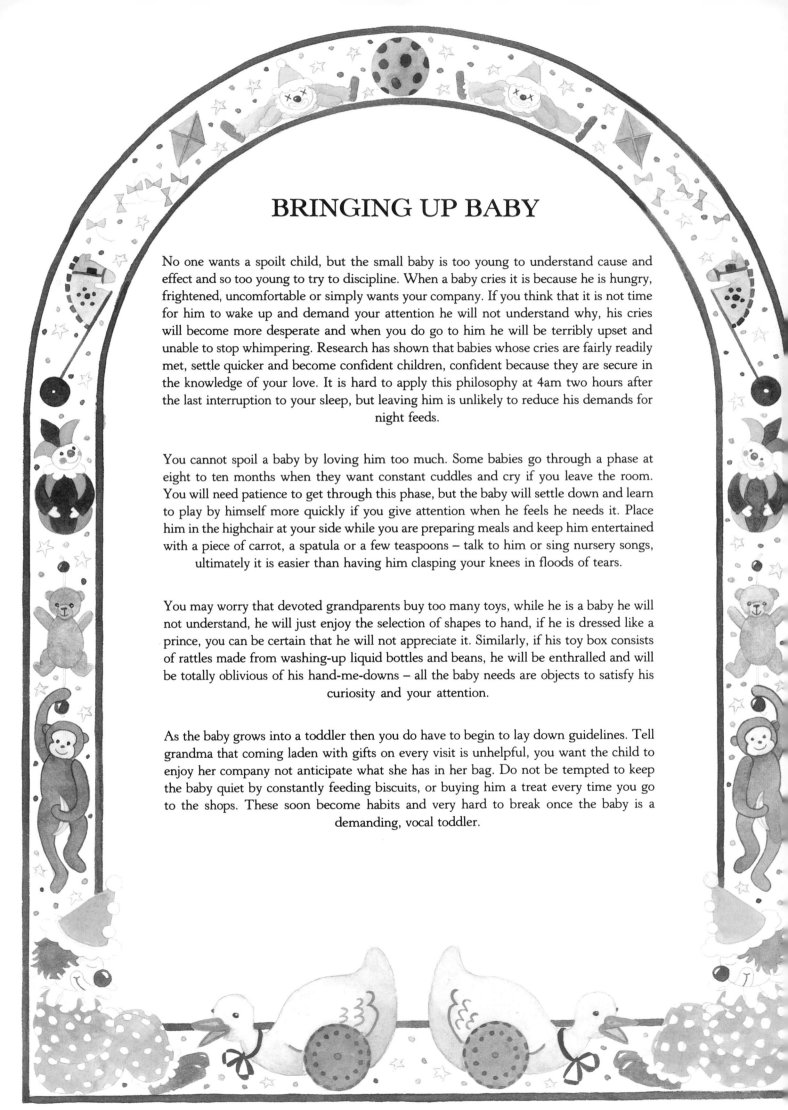

You will have to introduce a few rules once the baby becomes mobile. You will find that a lot of confrontation can be avoided by removing most breakable objects to high shelves or putting them away until he is old enough not to damage them. Keep the number of restricted things to a minimum but when you say 'no' you must mean it and you must be consistent. There is no point in saying 'no' and removing the baby from the cooker when it is hot but allowing him to touch it later when it is cold, he is too little to understand your reasoning. If most of the cupboards are out of bounds, have one which is not so that every time he tries to get in amongst the plates you remove him to the saucepan cupboard where he can do no damage.

If you do find yourself shouting at the baby do not be too hard on yourself, a mobile baby is very tiring and no one can be expected to be patient all the time. The baby will be startled at your anger but will not bear a grudge. Take a deep breath and take the baby to his toys and hand him something interesting.

Tips

Do begin to discipline your baby because young children like to have a framework of rules by which to measure their own behavior.

If your baby grabs a toy belonging to an older child, or something you do not want him to have, distract his attention by showing him another item, he will then release first object without a squeal.

Praise your child whenever he does something well or responds to your commands.

If the baby is still demanding night feeds at eight months he probably does not really need feeding. Try going in comforting the child and offering water or juice instead of milk, then put him back into his cot and settle him by playing a musical toy.

Some babies adopt comfort habits, maybe thumb sucking or fondness for a particular blanket or teddy. Do not think this implies that the baby is insecure, rather that he has discovered a way of comforting himself.

BABY
ON THE MOVE

(record Baby's age)

First stands with help

First steps alone

First found standing in cot

Learns to climb stairs

First stands alone

Learns to run

Walks with help

Learns to jump

Memories

Photograph of Baby on the move

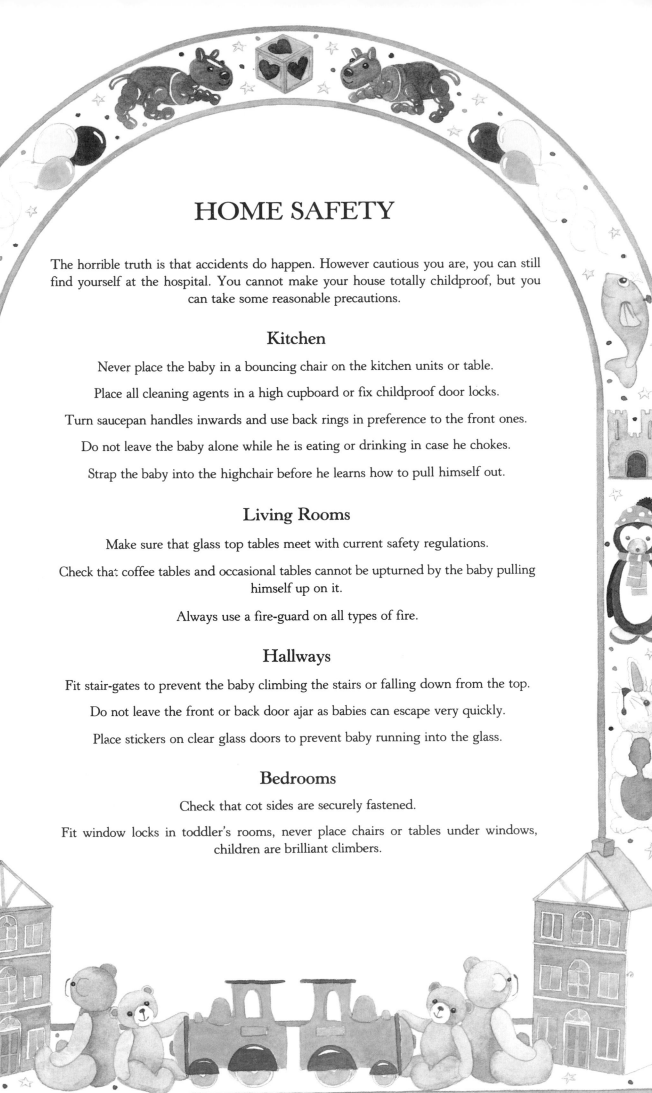

HOME SAFETY

The horrible truth is that accidents do happen. However cautious you are, you can still find yourself at the hospital. You cannot make your house totally childproof, but you can take some reasonable precautions.

Kitchen

Never place the baby in a bouncing chair on the kitchen units or table.

Place all cleaning agents in a high cupboard or fix childproof door locks.

Turn saucepan handles inwards and use back rings in preference to the front ones.

Do not leave the baby alone while he is eating or drinking in case he chokes.

Strap the baby into the highchair before he learns how to pull himself out.

Living Rooms

Make sure that glass top tables meet with current safety regulations.

Check that coffee tables and occasional tables cannot be upturned by the baby pulling himself up on it.

Always use a fire-guard on all types of fire.

Hallways

Fit stair-gates to prevent the baby climbing the stairs or falling down from the top.

Do not leave the front or back door ajar as babies can escape very quickly.

Place stickers on clear glass doors to prevent baby running into the glass.

Bedrooms

Check that cot sides are securely fastened.

Fit window locks in toddler's rooms, never place chairs or tables under windows, children are brilliant climbers.

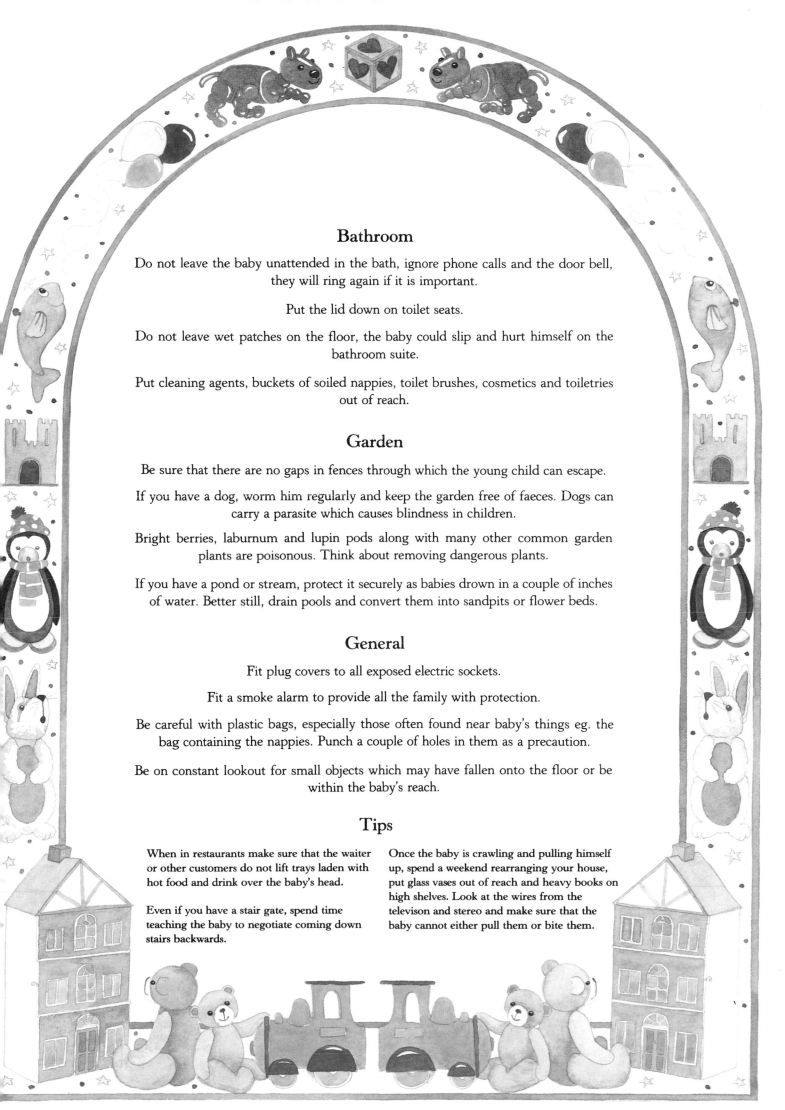

Bathroom

Do not leave the baby unattended in the bath, ignore phone calls and the door bell, they will ring again if it is important.

Put the lid down on toilet seats.

Do not leave wet patches on the floor, the baby could slip and hurt himself on the bathroom suite.

Put cleaning agents, buckets of soiled nappies, toilet brushes, cosmetics and toiletries out of reach.

Garden

Be sure that there are no gaps in fences through which the young child can escape.

If you have a dog, worm him regularly and keep the garden free of faeces. Dogs can carry a parasite which causes blindness in children.

Bright berries, laburnum and lupin pods along with many other common garden plants are poisonous. Think about removing dangerous plants.

If you have a pond or stream, protect it securely as babies drown in a couple of inches of water. Better still, drain pools and convert them into sandpits or flower beds.

General

Fit plug covers to all exposed electric sockets.

Fit a smoke alarm to provide all the family with protection.

Be careful with plastic bags, especially those often found near baby's things eg. the bag containing the nappies. Punch a couple of holes in them as a precaution.

Be on constant lookout for small objects which may have fallen onto the floor or be within the baby's reach.

Tips

When in restaurants make sure that the waiter or other customers do not lift trays laden with hot food and drink over the baby's head.

Even if you have a stair gate, spend time teaching the baby to negotiate coming down stairs backwards.

Once the baby is crawling and pulling himself up, spend a weekend rearranging your house, put glass vases out of reach and heavy books on high shelves. Look at the wires from the televison and stereo and make sure that the baby cannot either pull them or bite them.

BABY'S FUN AND GAMES
(record Baby's age)

Learns to clap hands	Plays pat-a-cake
Dances to music	Waves good-bye
Enjoys banging toys	Learns to use a slide
Plays peep-bo	Enjoys first tricycle

Memories

Photograph of Baby's fun and games

FUN AND GAMES

You are the most entertaining object in the world to a new baby, but given that you cannot always be with her you will want to provide her with toys. Babies learn about the world through colour, texture and sound so choose toys that combine these features. A baby gym is brilliant for a small baby as the parts are colourful, they move in a variety of directions and make an assortment of noises. These are not cheap but there is a huge assortment of smaller rattles and ingenious toys for small babies on the market.

Bold colours are easier for the young baby to see than pretty pastel colours so place strongly coloured pictures and bright toys close to the baby's bouncing chair and around his crib. A colourful mobile may entertain the baby for some time after waking or may attract his attention if it is placed above the changing mat.

Babies also learn by touching and exploring objects with the mouth. First toys will end up in the mouth so should be easy to grasp should provide a good surface to bite on. Check that soft toys are washable, that seams are well sewn and that eyes and other small parts are well attached. Avoid very cheap baby toys, it is always better to buy one with a safety label.

As the baby develops he is ready for toys that do things. The simplest of these is a ball which rolls away and can be chased. A duck on a string is great fun when you are about ten months old and a pop-up toys are wonderful for introducing the concept of cause and effect. Toys do not need to be expensive to be successful. A mobile baby will love a cardboard box, will enjoy playing 'where's baby gone' with a sheet and will happily bang a saucepan lid with a wooden spoon. Once the baby is up on his feet he will enjoy pushing a baby walker even if he has not yet taken his first step. He will gain confidence on his feet and will expect you to be very impressed with him as he marches across the floor.

From about nine months a baby will enjoy sitting on your knee with a board book, he may be pointing by this age and will point out animals or objects in the pictures which you will name and so help him with his language development. Along the same lines, he will enjoy hearing you recite nursery rhymes and activity rhymes such as 'Round and round the garden' and 'Ride a cock horse'. You may not have a singing voice you would inflict on your worst enemy, but your baby will think it wonderful. When you are sure no one is around to tease you, sing all the old songs from your own childhood to the baby. It will keep him amused while you prepare lunch or do the laundry.

Tips

Make a mobile from a wire coat hanger and tie on coloured ribbons, plastic flowers, tinsel, a screwed up ball of coloured paper, etc. You can change the objects frequently to hold the baby's attention.

Very small babies are particularly fascinated by faces. Draw silly faces on paper plates and arrange them around his cot.

Babies grow out of toys quickly so accept second-hand toys gratefully. For your own peace of mind, wipe with a mild disinfectant before passing to a young baby.

Set aside a table top out of baby's reach on which an older child can keep precious toys and those with small parts which the baby might swallow.

BABY'S FIRST BIRTHDAY

How the day was celebrated

Mother and father's presents

Baby's reactions

Birthday cake

Visitors and presents

Photograph of Baby's first birthday

SOLID FEEDING

When the baby is around three to four months you may wish to introduce solid food to supplement his milk feeds. Weaning is a slow process and if the baby shows no signs of wanting to suck food off a spoon, leave it for a week and try again. At first solid food is a supplement to the baby's milk, it is unlikely that the baby will be eating three meals a day for several months. Never rush the baby onto solid feeding, and if there is a history of allergies in your family, talk to your doctor as you may be advised to delay weaning until the child is about six months.

Start mixed feeding with one teaspoon plain baby rice made up with about one tablespoon of formula, breast milk or water. It should be quite runny or the baby will gag. Hold the spoon to the baby's lips and let her suck off the food, finish the feed as normal with a bottle. After a few days on rice, a second solid can be introduced, often this is pureed stewed apple sweetened with a little honey or sugar. Do not rush to introduce new flavours, it is sensible to leave at least three days between each new food, that way you will be able to identify any that upset his tummy or that cause a rash.

As the early foods consist of pureed fruit and vegetables, it is easy to prepare these at home and puree them in a food processor, mouli or through a sieve (acid fruits must be pressed through a nylon sieve). This works out much cheaper than buying processed food and you have the satisfaction of knowing exactly what the baby is eating. Freeze excess puree in ice cube trays, this enables you to quickly defrost small quantities for another feed.

Good First Foods

Cooked Pureed Vegetables

Carrot
Cauliflower
Courgette
Green beans
Leeks
Parsnip
Peas
Potato
Sweet potato
Sweet corn
Swede

Pureed Fruit

Avocado
Stewed apple
Melon
Pear
Peaches
Fresh or stewed dried apricots
Banana

As the baby becomes used to the taste of fruit and vegetables you may also introduce, pasteurised cheeses, cooked and pureed chicken, turkey and white fish. Eggs are introduced at about 6 months, make sure that they are well cooked. A variety of pulses and other meats can be given at this time. By about ten months the baby will be able to eat most of the foods that you prepare for the family. Continue to avoid spicy or highly flavoured foods and keep additives down to a minimum.

Jars of baby food and granulated foods are available in a wide variety of tastes. These are wonderful convenience foods, and provide the baby with a vitamin and mineral supplement. However, the baby will be getting all his vitamin requirements from milk feeds at first and when this is replaced by solid foods he will get a range of nutrients from a variety of foods. Most weaned babies are also given a multivitamin supplement available from the clinic. All parents worry about the introduction of solids, do seek reassurance from the professionals and other mothers.

There is no right time to stop breast feeding, it is when you feel that the baby has had a good start, or you are getting very tired, or maybe it is because you are returning to work. Unless otherwise advised by the doctor, stop breast feeding slowly, replace the midday breast feed with a bottle, then a couple of days later replace the evening feed. This way your breasts will adjust the production of milk to meet the reduced demand and you will not have overfull, painful breasts.

Tips

Wash out baby food jars and use to store homemade meals in the freezer.

Keep a portion of granulated food or a jar in the changing bag in case of emergencies.

After you stop breast feeding your breasts will look and feel small, in a couple of months the fat is laid down on the breasts and they will look like new again.

If your baby will not feed from a teat, try a feeder mug at about 5 months. Select the one with the smallest holes.

Babies often become constipated when solids are introduced. Feed fruit instead of cereals or try dissolving a teaspoon of brown sugar in boiling water, once cool, feed to the baby off a spoon.

BABY'S
ACCOMPLISHMENTS
(record Baby's age)

Learns to drink from a cup

Learns to eat alone

Recognises objects when asked

Learns basic colours

Learns parts of the body

Learns animal noises

First word

The word was

Memories

Obeys simple instructions

Learns to wash hands

First brushes teeth

First haircut

Helps with getting dressed

Opens doors

Draws with crayons

Learns to use potty

Memories

Photograph of Baby's accomplishments

Photograph of Baby's accomplishments

Photograph of Baby's accomplishments

Photograph of Baby's accomplishments

Photograph of Baby's accomplishments

CHILDCARE

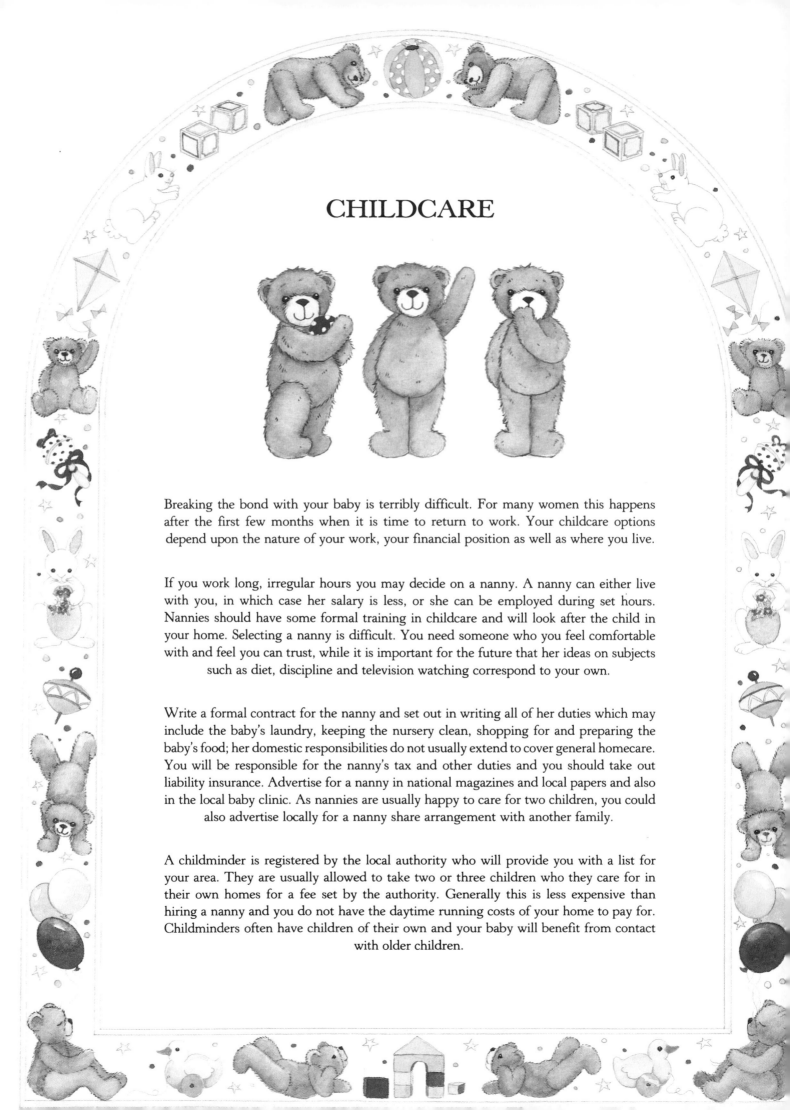

Breaking the bond with your baby is terribly difficult. For many women this happens after the first few months when it is time to return to work. Your childcare options depend upon the nature of your work, your financial position as well as where you live.

If you work long, irregular hours you may decide on a nanny. A nanny can either live with you, in which case her salary is less, or she can be employed during set hours. Nannies should have some formal training in childcare and will look after the child in your home. Selecting a nanny is difficult. You need someone who you feel comfortable with and feel you can trust, while it is important for the future that her ideas on subjects such as diet, discipline and television watching correspond to your own.

Write a formal contract for the nanny and set out in writing all of her duties which may include the baby's laundry, keeping the nursery clean, shopping for and preparing the baby's food; her domestic responsibilities do not usually extend to cover general homecare. You will be responsible for the nanny's tax and other duties and you should take out liability insurance. Advertise for a nanny in national magazines and local papers and also in the local baby clinic. As nannies are usually happy to care for two children, you could also advertise locally for a nanny share arrangement with another family.

A childminder is registered by the local authority who will provide you with a list for your area. They are usually allowed to take two or three children who they care for in their own homes for a fee set by the authority. Generally this is less expensive than hiring a nanny and you do not have the daytime running costs of your home to pay for. Childminders often have children of their own and your baby will benefit from contact with older children.

Some businesses have a workplace creche or subsidized nursery facilities. There are also private and local authority run nurseries some of which take babies, others take toddlers. The staff to child ratio is often lower in a nursery than in the other options discussed, but they are properly equipped and run by trained staff who can stimulate your child in an interesting environment. The nursery option gains in popularity as the baby grows into a child, by the time she is three, she will really benefit from the social and developmental skills she learns in the nursery.

By the age of three, even the mother who has stayed at home with her baby should consider sending her child to playgroup or nursery. It is essential that young children learn to mix, share and play with others away from the protection of mother's ever watchful eye.

Saying goodbye to a young baby is more difficult for you than for the baby, but as she becomes more aware of the world she will go through a phase of crying and clinging to you as you say goodbye. You will feel terrible, but the only way to deal with this is not to prolong the agony and take your leave. Phone the minder from work for reassurance, most babies settle a few moments after mother's departure only to burst into tears again when she reappears.

Tips

Do talk to other parents about their solutions to the childcare problems and talk about your own mixed feelings.

Spend some time with the nanny or minder so that you gain confidence in her before leaving the baby. The week before beginning work, leave the baby for an hour or two so that the first day is not too traumatic.

Mothers staying at home with baby should also have a break for the sake of the mother's sanity and to get the baby used to someone other than mum. Ask a friend or relation to have the baby from time to time.

Do not make any firm commitments at work before the baby is born. You may simply be unable to part from him.

If you think that your child will be overwhelmed by the playgroup or nursery, spend a few mornings there with him to increase his confidence before leaving him alone.

BABY'S FAVOURITES

At six months

_____
Food

_____
Toy

_____
Person

_____
Book

_____
Game

_____
Nursery rhyme

_____
Activity

At twelve months

_____
Food

_____
Toy

_____
Person

_____
Book

_____
Game

_____
Nursery rhyme

_____
Activity

At eighteen months

_____
Food

_____
Toy

_____
Person

_____
Book

_____
Game

_____
Nursery rhyme

_____
Activity

Photograph of Baby's favourites

BABY'S BEST FRIENDS

Special friends (names and ages)

First plays with other children

Favourite games with friends

Friends birthday parties

Favourite pets

Photograph of Baby's best friends

BABY'S FIRST HOLIDAY

Holidays with young children can be great fun, but their needs must be uppermost in your mind while you are planning your family holiday. If selecting a holiday from a brochure, choose one that says that children are catered for as that usually means that they have better facilities for children. Also check that the transfer from the airport to the hotel is fairly swift – a six hour coach journey can be intolerable.

Self-catering is often a good option especially once the baby is on solid foods. Take a small sieve with you so that you can puree cooked vegetables and peeled fruit, even in outlandish places the local produce is usually good. A mixture of pureed boiled courgettes and tomatoes is a good staple, and babies love watermelon, mangos and peaches. Dried instant food is also good on holiday as boiled water is usually easy to obtain. These foods also mix up from cold water, which means you can boil some in the morning, place in a bottle and mix up a feed in case of emergencies. If you are self-catering you can sterilize bottles, feeding spoons and teats by boiling for 10 minutes.

If you are travelling to a warm climate, make sure that you take a sunshade for your buggy. A very thin cotton sheet is useful to cover the baby's sensitive skin from the sun without overheating. Also apply high factor sun block to the baby's skin, and moisturise well after bathing. The baby should wear a hat outside and also make sure that the back of her neck is protected from the sun to prevent sunstroke. The baby will need more liquids than in cooler climates, simple boiled water is the best. Don't forget that breast-feeding mothers will need more fluids as well.

A young baby is very portable. A barge holiday, for instance is ideal for a baby up to about seven months when she becomes mobile. You have full catering facilities and the baby is entertained by the constantly moving scene. The difficult period is from about 7 to 24 months, when the baby is first mobile, until she learns to follow your commands. An active baby will eat sand, want to crawl on wet grass and will object to being restrained for more than a few minutes – this is maybe the time to take holidays at the home of an indulgent relation or friend – they might even babysit and give you an evening out.

Once the child is about two you will rediscover the attractions of a warm, seaside holiday. Small children will play for hours with a bucket and spade, they will need close supervision but they are a delight to watch and very entertaining.

Tips

Don't forget that babies need passports and visas although they can be added to either parent's documents. Make sure you send in application forms well in advance of the holiday.

Special guides are produced for good family holidays, these have been tried and tested – choosing one of these may be sensible for the first holiday.

Do make it clear on holiday application forms that you have a baby and check that a cot can be provided.

Encourage the young child to wear armbands whenever close to the seashore, accidents happen very quickly.

Take a bag of small surprises as travel entertainment.

If flying, ask for bulkhead seats when booking as these have more leg room and fixtures for special baby cots.

BABY'S FIRST HOLIDAY

Location

Date   Baby's age

Who went

How we got there

Holiday activities

Baby's reactions

Photograph of Baby's first holiday

BABY'S SECOND BIRTHDAY

How the day was celebrated

Mother and father's presents

Baby's reactions

Birthday cake

Visitors and presents

Photograph of Baby's second birthday